TRANSFORMERS ROBOTS IN DISGUISE

501 THINGS TO FIND

igloobooks

YOUR MISSION

BUMBLEBEE AND THE AUTOBOTS HAVE LOCATED DECEPTICON ISLAND, THE LARGEST REMAINING PART OF THE CRASHED PRISON SHIP, THE ALCHEMOR.

HOWEVER, THEY SOON LEARN THAT STEELJAW IS IN CHARGE, LEADING A DECEPTICON ARMY. THE AUTOBOTS NEED YOUR ASSISTANCE!

HELP BUMBLEBEE AND THE REST OF THE TEAM TO SEEK OUT THE DECEPTICONS AND DEFEAT STEELJAW BY COMPLETING ALL THE SEARCH-AND-FIND ACTIVITIES.

MISSION ACCEPTED!

BEFORE STARTING, PRACTISE ON THE OPPOSITE PAGE BY FINDING THE CORRECT AMOUNT OF EACH AUTOBOT IN THE LARGER IMAGE. WHEN YOU'VE FOUND THEM ALL, YOU'RE READY TO EMBARK ON YOUR MISSION!

3
6
9

AUTOBOTS ASSEMBLE

ONLY THE BEST CAN TAKE DOWN THOSE DECEPTICONS. CAN YOU FIND THE RIGHT NUMBER OF EACH DIFFERENT AUTOBOT HEAD IN THE JUMBLED PICTURE ABOVE?

1

2

3

4

5

6

7

8

9

10

KEEP THE COGS TURNING

IT MAY LOOK LIKE A MESS, BUT THE SCRAPYARD IS THE HOME OF THE AUTOBOTS. FIXIT LOVES TO REPAIR THINGS TO MAKE SURE EVERYTHING IS IN WORKING ORDER. CAN YOU FIND ALL THE COGS LISTED?

1
2
3
4
5
6
7
8
10
16

THE AUTOBOTS

GRIMLOCK

A TOUGH AND TENACIOUS DINOBOT, GRIMLOCK JOINED THE AUTOBOTS SIMPLY BECAUSE HE DIDN'T WANT TO MISS OUT ON THE FUN! HE MAY BE RECKLESS AND A LITTLE CLUMSY, BUT GRIMLOCK IS POWERFUL AND HEADSTRONG ENOUGH TO FIGHT HIS WAY OUT OF ANY PROBLEM.

BUMBLEBEE

AS LEADER OF THE AUTOBOTS, BUMBLEBEE IS AN ENERGETIC AND ENTHUSIASTIC ROBOT, WHO HOLDS A NO-NONSENSE APPROACH WHEN IN THE FIELD. ALTHOUGH HE IS STILL FIGURING OUT WHAT IT MEANS TO BE A GREAT LEADER, BUMBLEBEE ALWAYS LEARNS FROM HIS MISTAKES AND ENSURES THE JOB GETS DONE.

STRONGARM

STRONGARM IS A VERY COURAGEOUS ROBOT WHO LOVES HER CAREER IN LAW ENFORCEMENT. SHE IS ALWAYS WILLING TO THROW HERSELF INTO ANY DANGEROUS SITUATION IF IT MEANS SHE GETS TO CATCH A TARGET! SOMETIMES HER KEENNESS FOR HER JOB MEANS SHE DOESN'T ALWAYS GEL WITH HER FELLOW AUTOBOTS, PARTICULARLY SIDESWIPE.

OPTIMUS PRIME

OPTIMUS PRIME IS A STERN AND SERIOUS COMMANDER, WHO IS DEVOTED TO PROTECTING INNOCENT LIFE. HE ACTS AS A SPIRITUAL LEADER TO BUMBLEBEE AND HIS TEAM. OPTIMUS PRIME HAS ALREADY WITNESSED THE DEVASTATION AND DESTRUCTION CAUSED BY MEGATRON, AND IS DETERMINED IT WON'T HAPPEN TO EARTH.

WINDBLADE

A THOUSAND YEARS AGO, WINDBLADE WAS GIVEN A MISSION BY PRIMUS HIMSELF TO HUNT DECEPTICONS. AS A RESULT OF HER ENHANCED FIGHTING ABILITIES AND AN INCREDIBLE INSTINCT FOR FINDING DECEPTICONS, WINDBLADE HAS ESTABLISHED HERSELF AS A FORCE TO BE RECKONED WITH.

FIXIT

ONCE STRANDED ON THE PRISON SHIP, ALCHEMOR, FIXIT IS A MINI-CON AUTOBOT WHO OFTEN ACTS AS MISSION CONTROL. FIXIT SPENDS HIS DAYS MAINTAINING AND REPAIRING CYBERTRONIAN TECHNOLOGY AND CAN TACKLE JUST ABOUT ANY REPAIR JOB. HE DOES HAVE A FEW GLITCHES AND CAN GET LOCKED IN A VERBAL LOOP.

SIDESWIPE

A MASTER AT STAYING COOL UNDER PRESSURE, SIDESWIPE IS A BIT OF A SHOW-OFF AND TENDS TO LOOK AFTER HIMSELF FIRST. SIDESWIPE CAN BE A REBEL AND HIS OVERLY COMPETITIVE NATURE CAN ANNOY HIS FELLOW AUTOBOTS, BUT HE ALWAYS COMES THROUGH FOR HIS TEAM. HE'S QUICK WITH HIS WORDS AND ENJOYS NOTHING MORE THAN DEFEATING HIS OPPONENT.

IN ORDER TO GET ONTO DECEPTICON ISLAND, GRIMLOCK IS GOING TO BE DISGUISED AS A DECEPTICON. WHILE GRIMLOCK TRANSITIONS INTO ONE OF THE ENEMY, CAN YOU SPOT THE RIGHT AMOUNT OF EACH SYMBOL?

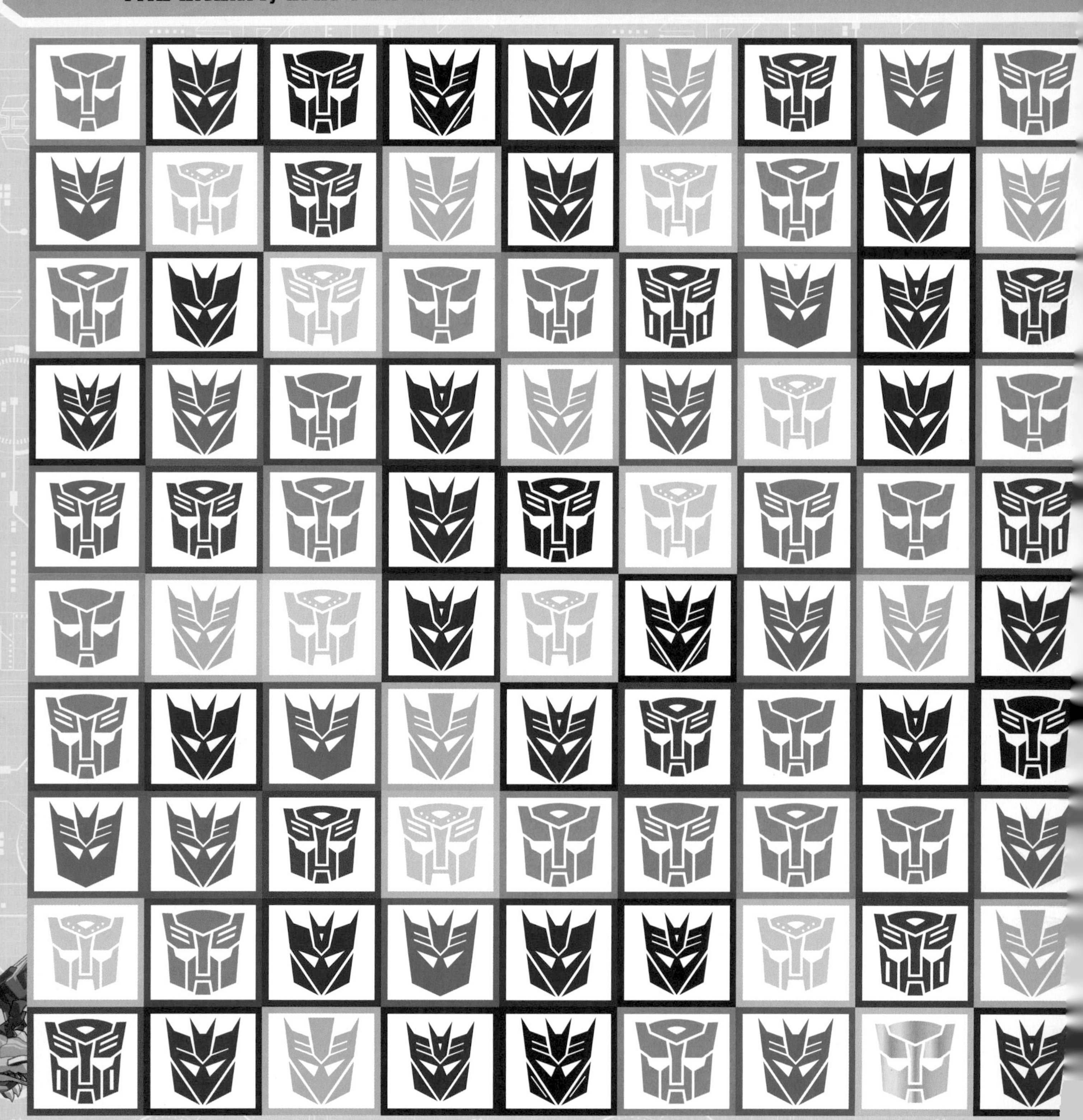

1
2
3
4
5
6
7
8
9
10

DECEPTICON DATA

FIXIT HAS SUCCESSFULLY LOCATED THE WHEREABOUTS OF STEELJAW'S SHIP. LOOK CAREFULLY AT THE DIGITAL SCREEN BELOW AND SEE IF YOU CAN FIND THE RIGHT AMOUNT OF EACH ICON.

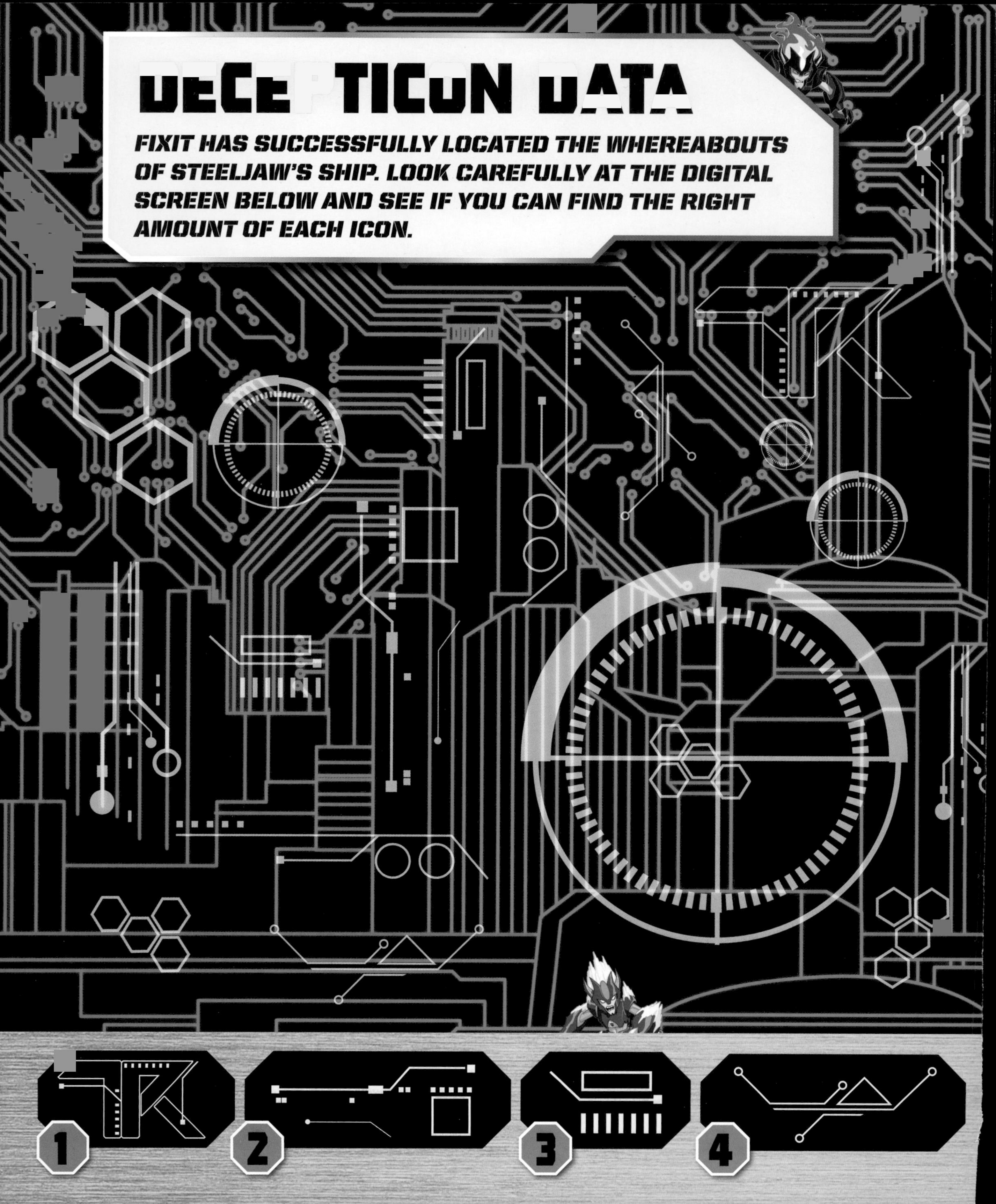

5
6
7
8

[illegible]EV U[illegible] AND [illegible]OLL OUT!

THE AUTOBOTS ARE READY TO GO. SEE IF YOU CAN SPOT THE VEHICLES LISTED IN THE SCENE BELOW, AS THE TEAM MAKE THEIR WAY TO DECEPTICON ISLAND.

5
6
10
12

STEELJAW'S SERVANTS

THE AUTOBOTS ARRIVE AND, THANKS TO GRIMLOCK, THEY MAKE IT PAST THE GUARDS. THE TEAM IS SHOCKED TO SEE HOW MANY MINI-CONS ARE UNDER STEELJAW'S CONTROL. LOOK AT THE SCENE BELOW AND SEE IF YOU CAN SPOT ALL THE MINI-CONS.

2
4
6
8

DECEPTICON HUNTERS

THE AUTOBOTS FINALLY CONFRONT THEIR ENEMY! STEELJAW LAUGHS AS HE SHOWS THEM THAT HE HOLDS TWO DECEPTICON HUNTERS. CAN YOU FIND THE RIGHT AMOUNT OF DECEPTICON HUNTERS IN THE JUMBLED SCENE ABOVE?

6
7
8
9
10

STEELJAW!

STEELJAW IS READY TO BATTLE THE AUTOBOTS. LOOK AT THE SCENE AND SEE IF YOU CAN SPOT ALL THE DIFFERENT STEELJAW IMAGES.

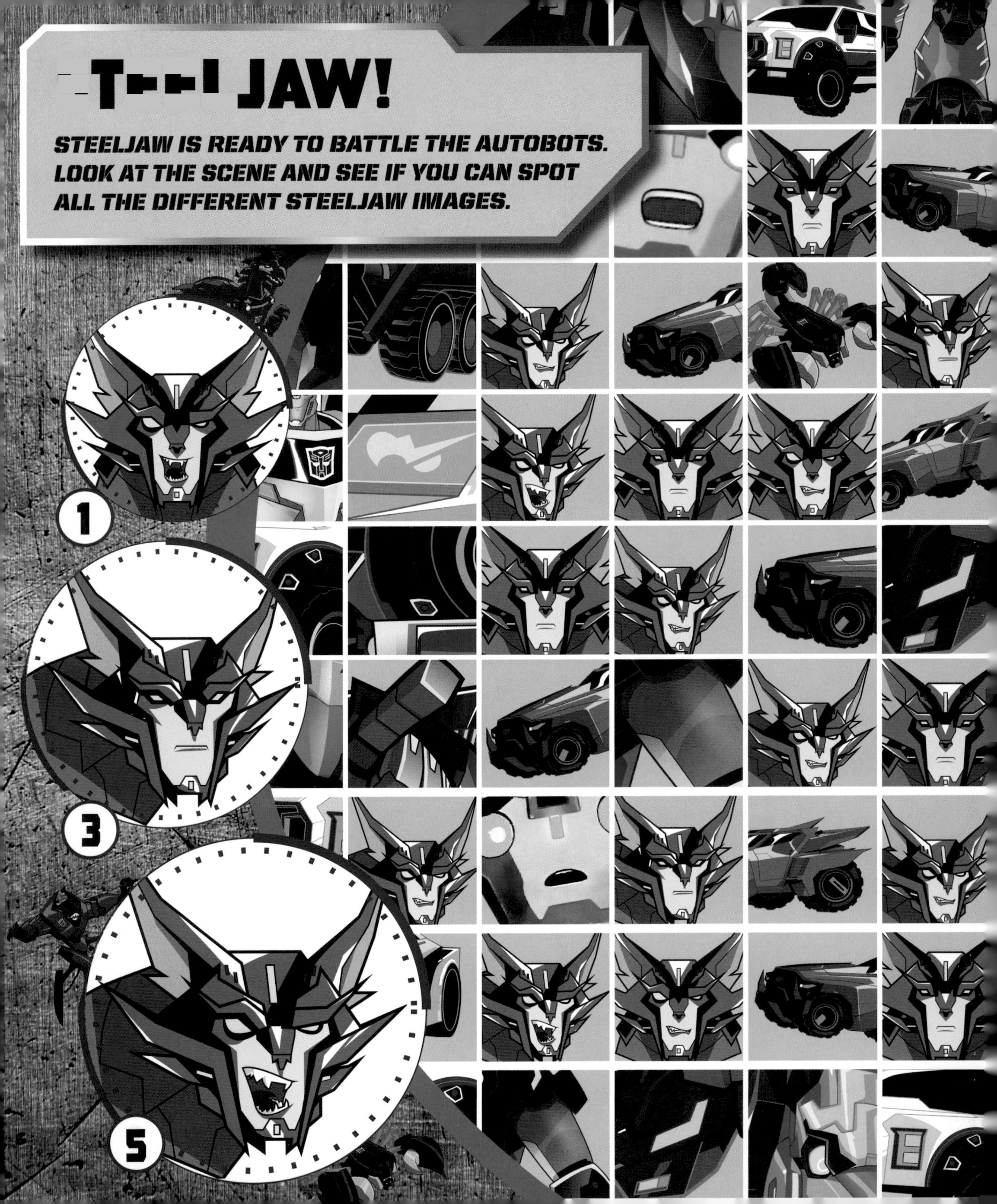

9
11
13

DECEPTICO
1
2
3
5
6
7
9
10

THE FIGHT IS ON! WHO WILL COME OUT ON TOP: THE AUTOBOTS OR THE DECEPTICONS? SEARCH THE COMIC STRIP TO SEE IF YOU CAN FIND ALL THE CLOSE-UPS TAKEN FROM THE IMAGES ON THE LEFT.

BONUS FINDS: DECEPTICON HUNTING

GOOD WORK, BUT THE MISSION IS NOT QUITE COMPLETE! THERE ARE 5 OF EACH OF THESE DECEPTICONS HIDDEN THROUGHOUT THE BOOK. GO BACK AND SEE IF YOU CAN FIND THEM.

THERE ARE ALSO 3 GOLD AUTOBOT SYMBOLS HIDING SOMEWHERE IN THE BOOK.